an extract from
muriel spark's

the comforters

with an enthusiast's view
by alan taylor

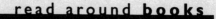

an extract from
muriel spark's

the comforters

with an enthusiast's view
by alan taylor

2003

Published by
Scottish Book Trust
Scottish Book Centre
137 Dundee Street
Edinburgh EH11 1BG

Tel: 0131 229 3663

**From April 2003 Scottish Book Trust will be moving its offices
to Sandeman House, 55 High Street, Edinburgh EH1 1SR.**

ISBN: 1 901077 11 X
Copyright © Scottish Book Trust, 2003

Published with the support of the Scottish Arts Council National
Lottery Fund and The Hugh Fraser Foundation.

Scottish
Arts Council
LOTTERY FUNDED

The Comforters is published by Penguin
ISBN: 0 140 01911 1

Extract copyright © Muriel Spark, 1957

Series design by Caleb Rutherford   eidetic
Printed in the UK by Cox & Wyman, Reading, Berkshire

contents

read **around books**

There is no shortage of fiction on the shelves of our bookshops – quite the opposite – but finding one that shouts out 'this is what you are looking for' is getting harder and harder as the number of books published goes up with each passing year. Too often we open a new book with expectation and enthusiasm only to discover disappointment and to struggle to get beyond page thirty. When we do find a book we really enjoy the urge is there to tell friends, colleagues and family to read it too in the hope that they will share our delight.

Read Around Books goes one step further and puts that enthusiasm down in black and white in the hope that many more readers will discover the joys of reading the very finest fiction that has emerged from Scotland over the last one hundred years. **This is a chance to sample before you borrow or buy**. Others have found these books before you, the writing held them spellbound and even when finished, these books would not let their readers go.

Each of the first twelve of these highly collectable little guide books promotes a work of fiction by a writer who lives in Scotland, was born in Scotland or who has been influenced by Scotland (our definition of Scottish is generous). Together they offer a marvellous introduction to the very best of Scottish writing from the twentieth and the first few years of the twenty-first centuries.

In each you will find a substantial extract, the enthusiast's view of the book, starting points for discussion for readers' groups, a short biographical piece about the author, and suggestions for similar reads which act as a further gateway to fine fiction.

Jan Rutherford
Series editor, 2003

the enthusiast

Alan Taylor

Alan Taylor is Associate Editor for the *Sunday Herald*. He is also a well-known literary critic and newspaper diarist and one half of the underperforming Scottish team on BBC Radio Four's 'Round Britain Quiz'. The year 2000 saw the publication of *The Assassin's Cloak: An Anthology of the World's Greatest Diarists* (Canongate) which he co-edited with his wife Irene and which was ten years in the making.

the enthusiast's **view**

The Comforters

by Muriel Spark

Some writers have careers, others have vocations. Muriel Spark is one of the latter. For her, writing is as serious a calling as a nun's. But that does not mean to say she is pious or worthy or humourless. On the contrary, her work resonates with irreverent laughter and there are few pages in her extensive oeuvre that are not spiced with a witty line, bon mots or a memorable aphorism. Her aim, she has said, is to deal with important subjects in a light-hearted manner, almost as if they don't matter, which, needless to say, they do hugely.

But it is a risky strategy and one that is easily misunderstood. Moreover her books tend to be slender, which leads some commentators to dismiss them as slight. Again, nothing could be further from the truth. Underlying everything Spark writes is a rigorous examination of what makes us behave the way we do. What motivates and compels us. What makes us tick. In that regard her novels are like icebergs, the vast bulk of which lie beneath the surface.

The Comforters was her debut novel and it contains all the hallmarks which we now recognise as Sparkian. It is slim. It has a neurotic woman, Caroline Rose, as its heroine. The plot is improbable and fantastical. There is a cast of vibrant characters whom Dickens would recognise. It has unplumbed depths. And, of course, it is beautifully written, deeply disturbing and very funny, in inimitable, musical prose. Evelyn Waugh read it when it first appeared and was dismayed by how much better it was than his own, quite similar novel, *The Ordeal of Gilbert Pinfold*. *The Comforters*, he remarked, is 'brilliantly original and fascinating'.

Waugh correctly identified the theme of the novel as 'a Catholic novelist suffering from hallucinations'. This is Caroline who some critics have compared directly with her creator. This is understandable, though in the long run it is not particularly helpful except perhaps to biographers.

For example, we are told Caroline has 'been in Africa' and that she has 'a literary reputation'. Ditto Spark. Caroline goes to a Benedictine Priory to receive instruction from a Father Jerome; Spark, a convert to Catholicism, also received instruction at a similar priory. Caroline, we're told, 'excelled at packing a suitcase'. Perhaps Spark does as well. Then again, perhaps not. Pursuing autobiographical threads in novels may be fun but very often you find yourself at a dead-end.

What strikes you first of all, however, is the quality of the writing and the confident tone of voice of the author.

Spark's debut came rather late: she was almost forty when *The Comforters* appeared, which may explain why it feels so assured. In quick succession we are introduced to the cast: Laurence Manders, a sports announcer on the BBC; his grandmother, Louisa Jepp; Laurence's mother, Lady Helena, and her husband, Edwin; Mrs Jepp's triumvirate of co-conspirators, Mervyn Hogarth and his son Andrew, and Mr Webster the baker; Baron Stock; and last, but by no means least, Georgina Hogg.

Spark portrays each so memorably that you can picture them instantly. Mrs Jepp, a septuagenarian gypsy, is short, 'and seen from the side especially, her form resembles a neat double potato just turned up from the soil with its small round head, its body from which hangs the roots, her two thin legs below her full brown skirt and corpulence'. Georgina Hogg is an ignorant cradle Catholic with 'a colossal bosom'. Baron Stock is a bookseller in Charing Cross Road, 'one of those which keep themselves exclusively intellectual. "Intellect-u-al", the Baron pronounced it. He would say, "Of course there are no intellect-u-als in England".' Most significantly, Caroline has bouts of anorexia and thinks she may be going potty, driven crazy by the tap-tappity-tap of a typewriter and a chorus of voices. Her brain, we're told, is like 'a Guy Fawkes night', with ideas cracking off in all directions.

Bizarre and improbable as all this may sound, Spark's art is to make it seem suspiciously normal. Initially, Louisa Jepp appears to be a perfectly ordinary grandmother, first encountered ordering a loaf of wholemeal bread from a baker. What could be more mundane? But in the Sparkian view of the universe nothing is quite as it appears on the surface. Contravening the cliché of a little old lady, Louisa, it turns out, is the leader of a gang of smugglers, a seasoned crook who is in cahoots with the baker, who helps her by hiding diamonds in his loaves. 'If you won thirty thousand in the pool,' asks her grandson, 'what would you do?' 'Buy a boat,' she replies. 'Suitable for crossing the Channel.' Everything she does and says undermines her innocence.

Spark's intention is not to mirror reality. That would be too boring. Her raison d'être is to create literature which 'opens doors and windows on the mind'. 'I don't claim that my novels are truth,' she says. 'I claim that they are fiction out of which a kind of truth emerges.' The source of that truth in *The Comforters* is Caroline who, among other things, is a student of the structure of the novel. For her, Catholicism is the True Faith but she is not seduced automatically into believing that all Catholics are equally blessed. She is sceptical about miracles and enjoys baiting Georgina Hogg who claims she is in constant dialogue with 'Our Lady'. 'How do you know the words come from the Blessed Virgin?' Caroline asks, all the while thinking to herself: 'She desires the ecstasy of murdering me in some prolonged ritualistic orgy; she sees I am thin, angular, sharp, inquiring; she sees I am grisly about the truth; she sees I am well-dressed and good-looking. Perhaps she senses my weakness, my loathing of human flesh where the bulk outweighs the intelligence.'

Caroline is a conduit for Spark's own cracking ideas, her representative in fiction as a priest is for the Holy Father on earth. She says one thing while constantly mulling over others. She is also, despite her relationship with Laurence, a loner, trying desperately to make sense of the world and her place in it. She has friends, like Baron Stock, who are prepared to give her a bed for the night when the voices drive her out of her own, but they are unreliable. First, though, she must get to the bottom of the voices. How can she hear them when they can't be recorded? Ultimately, this leads to more complex questions: What is reality? Can a novel be real? If so, how?

Fans of Spark will recognise the recurrence of these mind-expanding themes throughout her work. They will also recognise her addiction to the unexplained and the supernatural, the appeal of hypnosis, seances, the occult, and the gamut of the criminal classes, from forgers, conmen and bigamists to blackmailers, thieves and murderers. For example, in her most recently published novel, *Aiding and Abetting*, which appeared in 2000, she entwines the true story of the disappearance of Lord Lucan, who allegedly battered his children's nanny to death before vanishing without trace, with an imaginary one of a fake stigmatic woman. It is an unlikely marriage but a very successful one. What makes it work is Spark's bold telling and her transparent lack of sentimentality.

It is a tradition which harks back to the Border ballads, which Spark learned to recite by heart at school in Edinburgh in the 1920s. In ballads such as the 'Twa

Corbies' and 'Sir Partick Spens' terrible events are related deadpan. It is a lesson Spark has off pat. For her appearances are invariably deceptive and unreliable, while motives are always questionable. She is as much a philosopher as she is a novelist.

It is vital, however, that readers, like the characters in the novel, are kept in the dark. In that regard, Spark is like a magician. It is only in hindsight that we begin to ponder more deeply and realise that what seemed straightforward was anything but. That we should be so convincingly and comprehensively taken in is the mark of a spellbinding storyteller revelling in the inseparability of farce and tragedy. *The Comforters* – which takes its title from the discomfortable comforters in the *Book of Job*, who, said Louis de Bernières, 'are possibly the most irritating characters in all of literature' – veers continually between the two, especially when Caroline and Georgina Hogg rub up against one another. The latter, 'a psychological thug', drives the former to the brink of insanity.

It is an almighty, spiritual struggle, albeit one that is told with the most delicate of touches. Can Caroline prevail? Will she ever be free of her demons? Like her creator, she wants to write a novel. Asked what it is to be about, she replies, 'Characters in a novel.' Of course, she could be describing *The Comforters*. Or could there be another voice murmuring in her ear, that of Muriel Spark, playing one of her delightful, devilish tricks? What a mischievous entertainer she is.

The extract

The Comforters

Chapter three

When Laurence returned to the cottage after posting his letter to Caroline his grandmother handed him a telegram.

He read it. 'It's from Caroline. She's back in London.'

'Yes, funny, I had a feeling it was from Caroline.' Louisa very often revealed a mild form of the gipsy's psychic faculties. 'Fancy, what a pity you've posted that letter to Liverpool.'

As Laurence set off to the post office again to telephone Caroline, he said, 'Shall I ask her to come down here?'

'Yes, certainly,' Louisa said with that inclination of her head which was a modified form of the regal gesture. When he was small she used to tell Laurence 'Don't just answer "Yes"; say "Yes, certainly", that's how Queen Mary always answers.'

'How do you know that, Grandmother?'

'A person told me.'

'Are you sure the person was telling the truth?'

'Oh yes, certainly.'

'Tell Caroline,' Louisa called after him, 'that I have some blackberries in my tins,' meaning by this to tell Laurence of her genuine desire for Caroline's visit.

'All right, I will.'

'And ask the post office to give you back the letter. There's no reason to send it all the way to Liverpool.'

'Oh, they won't fish it out without a fuss,' Laurence told her. 'They never give you back a letter, once it's posted. Not without a fuss.'

'Oh, what a pity!'

'It doesn't matter,' Laurence said. 'I'll be seeing Caroline. I wonder why she left so soon?'

'Yes, I wonder why.'

Caroline's number was engaged when he rang. The sky had cleared and the autumn sun, low in the sky, touched the countryside. He decided to go to Ladle Sands, a half-hour's walk, from where he could try Caroline's number again, and by which time the pubs would be open. He was impatient to talk to Caroline. His desire to get her interested and involved in the mystery surrounding his grandmother was almost a fulfilment of a more compelling desire to assert the continuing pattern of their intimacy.

Laurence had no success with Caroline's phone that night. He pursued the exchange with mounting insistence on the urgency of getting through; they continued to reply in benumbed and fatalistic tones that the phone was out of order, it had been reported.

A queer buzzing sound brought Caroline to the telephone just before midnight. 'Your receiver has been off. We've been trying to get a call through from Sussex.' They were extremely irate.

'It hasn't been off,' said Caroline.

'It must have been misplaced. Please replace your receiver.'

'And the call? Are you putting it through?'

'No. The caller has gone now.'

Caroline thought, 'Well, he will ring in the morning.' She lay on her divan staring out at the night sky beyond her balcony, too tired to draw the curtains. She was warmed by the knowledge that Laurence was near to hand, wanting to speak to her. She could rely on him to take her side, should there be any difficulty with Helena over her rapid departure from St. Philumena's. On the whole she did not think there would be any difficulty with Helena.

Just then she heard the sound of a typewriter. It seemed to come through the wall on her left. It stopped, and was immediately followed by a voice remarking her own thoughts. It said: *On the whole she did not think there would be any difficulty with Helena.*

There seemed, then, to have been more than one voice: it was recitative, a chanting in unison. It was something like a concurrent series of echoes. Caroline jumped up and over to the door. There was no one on the landing or on the staircase outside. She returned to her sitting-room and shut the door. Everything was quiet. The wall, from which direction the sounds had come, divided her sitting-room from the first-floor landing of a house converted into flats. Caroline's flat occupied the whole of this floor. She had felt sure the sounds had come from the direction of the landing. Now she searched the tiny flat. The opposite wall separated the bed-sitting-room from the bathroom and kitchen. Everything was quiet there. She went out on to the balcony from where she could see the whole length of Queen's Gate. Two servicemen clattered up the street and turned into Cromwell Road. The neighbouring balconies were dark and empty. Caroline returned to the room, closed the windows, and drew the curtains.

She had taken the flat four weeks ago. The house held six flats, most of which were occupied by married couples or young men who went out to their offices every day. Caroline knew the other tenants only by sight, greeting them in passing on the staircase. There were occasional noises at night, when someone had a party, but usually the house was quiet. Caroline tried to recall the tenants in the flat above hers. She was not certain; they all passed her landing on their way upstairs and she herself had never gone beyond the first floor.

A typewriter and a chorus of voices: What on earth are they up to at this time of night? Caroline wondered. But what worried her were the words they had used, coinciding so exactly with her own thoughts.

Then it began again. Tap-tappity-tap; the typewriter. And again, the voices: Caroline ran out on to the landing, for it seemed quite certain the sound came from that direction. No one was there. The chanting reached her as she returned to her room, with these words exactly:

What on earth are they up to at this time of night?
Caroline wondered. But what worried her were the words
they had used, coinciding so exactly with her own thoughts.

And then the typewriter again: tap-tap-tap. She was
rooted. 'My God!' she cried aloud. 'Am I going mad?'

As soon as she had said it, and with the sound of her
own voice, her mind was filled with an imperative need
to retain her sanity. It was the phrase 'Caroline
wondered' which arrested her. Immediately then, shaken
as she was, Caroline began to consider the possibilities,
whether the sounds she had heard were real or illusory.
While the thought terrified her that she was being
haunted by people – spirits or things – beings who had
read her thoughts, perhaps who could read her very
heart, she could not hope for the horrible alternative.
She feared it more; she feared that those sounds, so real
that they seemed to have come from the other side of the
wall, were hallucinations sent forth from her own mind.
Caroline sat for the next half-hour dazed and frightened,
wondering what to do. She dreaded a repetition of the
experience, yet prayed for some sign that her mind was
not unhinged. The question began to appear as one on
which she could herself decide; it was like being faced
with a choice between sanity and madness.

She had already concluded that the noise could not
have come from anyone in the house. The fact that her
feelings and reflections were being recorded seemed to
point to some invisible source, the issue being, was it
objectively real or was it imaginary? If the sounds came

from some real, invisible typewriter and voices, Caroline felt she was in danger, might go mad, but the experience was not itself a sign of madness. She was now utterly convinced that what she had heard was not the product of her own imagination. 'I am not mad. I'm not mad. See; I can reflect on the situation. I am being haunted. I am not haunting myself.' Meantime, she was trembling, frightened out of her wits, although her fear was not altogether blind.

Tap-click-tap. The voices again: *Meantime, she was trembling, frightened out of her wits, although her fear was not altogether blind.*

'Christ!' she said. 'Who *is* it there?' Although she had decided quite reasonably that no one in the house could be responsible for those sounds, none the less when she actually heard voices again, so clear, just behind the wall, she sprang up and began to search every corner of the flat, even under the divan, which was too low to conceal a human body; even in the little cupboard where the gas meter was fixed. The activity took the edge off her panic, and although she knew she would not find her tormentors in this way, she put all her energy into the search, moving furniture, opening and shutting doors. She suspected everything, however improbable; even that the sound might be contained in some quite small object – a box with a machine inside, operated from a distance. She acted upon these suspicions, examining everything closely in case she should find something strange.

There was suddenly a knocking from the ceiling.

Caroline propelled herself out of the flat and switched on the landing lights.

'Who's there?' she called up the stairs. 'Who is it?' Her voice was strained high with fear.

There was a movement above her, round the bend of the stair. A shuffle, and the opening of a door on the second landing. A woman's voice whispered fiercely, 'Keep quiet!'

Looking straight above her, Caroline saw the top half of a woman leaning over the banister, long wisps of grey hair falling over her face and her loose white garment showing between the banisters. Caroline screamed, was too late to stop herself when she recognized the woman as the occupant of the flat above.

'Are you drunk?' the angry tenant breathed at her. 'What do you mean by waking the house at this time of night? It's twenty-two minutes past one, and you've been banging about moving furniture and slamming doors for the last hour. I haven't slept a wink. I've got to go out to business in the morning.'

Another door opened on the second floor, and a man's voice said, 'Anything the matter? I heard a girl scream.' The woman scuttled back into her room, being undressed, and finished her complaint with her head only showing outside her door.

'It was that young woman downstairs. She's been making a disturbance for the past hour. Did you hear her?'

'I certainly heard a scream,' the man's voice said.

Caroline ran up a few steps so as to see the speakers

from the bend in the staircase. 'I got a terrible fright when I saw you,' she explained to the woman. 'Was that you knocking?'

'Indeed it was,' said the woman. 'I'll complain about this in the morning.'

'Were *you* using a typewriter?' Caroline began to inquire. She was helpless and shaky. 'I heard a typewriter, and voices.'

'You're mad!' said the woman, as she withdrew and shut the door. The young man had also retreated.

Caroline returned to her rooms, and, rapidly and stealthily, began to pack a small suitcase. She wondered where she would spend the rest of the night. A lonely hotel room was unthinkable, it would have to be a friend's house. She moved about, jerkily snatching at the necessary articles as if she expected some invisible hand, concealed in each object, to close over hers before she had got possession of it. She was anxious to make as little sound as possible, but in her nervousness bumped into the furniture and knocked over a glass dish. To protect herself from the noises of her movements, she contracted a muscle somewhere behind her nose and throat, which produced the effect in her ears as of a rustling breeze – it dulled the sound of her footsteps, making the whole operation sound quieter than it was.

Caroline pressed down the lid of her small case. She had decided where to go for the night. The Baron; he was awake, or at least available, at all hours. She opened the case again, remembering that she had packed her money; she would need it for the taxi to the Baron's flat in Hampstead. She was absorbed by the pressing need to get out of her flat at the earliest possible moment, and as she searched among her clothes she did not even notice, with her customary habit of self-observation, that she had thrown her night-things together anyhow. The difference between this frenzied packing operation and the deliberate care she had taken, in spite of her rage, to fold and fit her possessions into place at St Philumena's less than a day ago failed to register.

Tap-tick-tap. Tap. She did not even notice Click-tappity with her customary habit of self-observation, that she had thrown her night-things together anyhow. The difference between this frenzied packing operation and the deliberate care she had taken, in spite of her rage, to fold and fit her possessions into place at St Philumena's less than a day ago failed to register. Tap.

Coat – hat – handbag – suitcase; Caroline grabbed them and hustled out of the door, slamming it to. She rattled downstairs and out of the front door, which she slammed behind her. At the top of Queen's Gate, turning in from Old Brompton Road, she got a taxi and secured herself inside it with a slam of the door.

'It is quite a common thing,' Willi Stock said. 'Your brain is overworked.' This was the Baron speaking. He stood by the electric fire with its flicking imitation coals, sipping Curaçao.

Caroline sipped hers, curled up on the sofa, and crying. Absorbing the warmth of the fire and of the liquor, she felt a warmth of gratitude towards the Baron.

For the last hour he had been explaining her mental condition. She was consoled, not by the explanations, but by the fact of his recognizable face, by the familiar limitations of his mind, and by the reality of his warm flat and his bottle of Curaçao.

For the first time in her life, she felt that Willi Stock was an old friend. Regarding him in this category, she was able to secure her conscience in his company. For the Baron belonged to one of the half-worlds of Caroline's past, of which she had gradually taken leave; it was a society which she had half-forgotten, and of which she had come wholly to disapprove. It was over a year since she had last seen the Baron. But Laurence had kept up with him, had mentioned him from time to time, which confirmed Caroline in her feeling that she was in the company of an old friend. She greatly needed the protection of an old friend till daylight.

He said, 'Eleanor is away on tour just now.'

Caroline said, 'I know, Laurence had a postcard.'

Eleanor Hogarth was the Baron's mistress.

'Did he?' said the Baron. 'When was that?'

'Oh, last week sometime. He merely mentioned it.'

They called him the Baron because he called himself Baron Stock. Caroline was not aware from what aristocracy he derived his title: nor had anyone inquired; she was sure it was not self-imposed as some suggested. He came originally from the Belgian Congo, had travelled in the Near East, loitered in Europe, and finally settled in England, a naturalized British subject. That was fifteen years ago, and he was now nearing fifty.

Caroline had always felt that the Baron had native African blood, without being able to locate its traces in any one feature. She had been in Africa, and had a sense of these things. It was a matter of casual curiosity to her; but she had noticed, some years ago, when Africa's racial problems were being discussed in company with the Baron, he had denounced the blacks with ferocious bitterness, out of all proportion to the occasion. This confirmed Caroline's judgement; there was, too, an expression of pathos which at times appeared on the Baron's face, which she had seen in others of concealed mixed colour; and there was something about the whites of his eyes; what it was she did not know. And altogether, having observed these things, she did not much care.

The Baron had set up a bookshop in Charing Cross Road, one of those which keep themselves exclusively intellectual. 'Intellect-u-al,' the Baron pronounced it. He would say, 'Of course there are no intellect-u-als in England.'

It had been the delight of Caroline and Laurence to recall the day when they looked in on the Baron at Charing Cross Road, to find him being accosted by a tiny woman with the request:

'D'you have any railway books for children?'

The Baron reared high and thin on the central expanse of grey carpet and regarded her silently for half a second.

'Railway books for children,' she repeated. 'Books with pictures of trains and railways.'

The Baron said: 'Railway books for children, Madam? I do not think so, Madam.' His arm languidly indicated the shelves. 'We have Histor-ay, Biograph-ay, Theolog-ay, Theosoph-ay, Psycholog-ay, Religio-n, Poetr-ay, but railway books for children ... Try Foyles across the road, Madam.'

He raised his shoulders and eyebrows as he turned to Laurence and Caroline. 'My father,' he said, 'knew a man in the Belgian Diplomatic Service who was the author of a railway book for children. It was very popular and sold quickly. A copy was sent to a family in Yugoslavia. Of course, the book contained a code message. The author was revising the book for the second edition when he was arrested. That story is my total experience of railway books for children. Have you read this work on Kafka? – it has just come in, my darlings, my Laurence and my Caroline.'

In this way, Baron Stock was an old friend.

Caroline lay in the dark warm room on a made-up sofa bed. The Baron had left her just after four had struck. She had stopped crying. In case she should want them, the Baron had left a bottle of aspirins on a chair by the sofa. Caroline reached out for the bottle, unscrewed the cap and extracted the twist of cotton wool which she had hoped to find. She stuffed a piece in each ear. Now she was alone, it seemed to her that she had been playing a false role with the Baron. It was the inevitable consequence of her arrival at his flat in a panic, at a late hour; 'Willi! Let me in, I've been hearing voices!'

After that, she was forced to accept his protection, his friendliness; was glad of it. And when he settled her by the fire:

'Caroline, *my* dear, how slender and febrile you've become! What kind of voices? How extremely interesting. Was it a religi-ous experience?'

She had begun to weep, to apologize.

'Caroline, *my* dear, as you know, I never go to bed. Seriously, I never go to bed unless it's the last possible alternative. I am delighted beyond words – Caroline, my dear, I am honoured – your distress, my dear – if you can realize how I feel.'

And so she had to play the part. Now, alone in the dark, she thought, 'I should have faced it out at the flat. I shouldn't have run away.'

The Baron, of course, was convinced she was suffering from a delusion.

'It happens to many many people, my dear. It is quite nothing to worry about. If the experience should recur you will have a course of analysis or take some pills and the voices will go away. But I doubt that the phenomenon will recur. You have been under a considerable strain from what I hear of your severed relations with Laurence.'

'We haven't parted, really, you know.'

'But you now have separate establishments?'

'Yes, I've got rooms in Kensington. Laurence is keeping on the flat for the time being. He's away in the country. I must get in touch with him tomorrow, first thing.' She gave the deliberate impression of not wanting to talk any more.

'In Sussex? With Mrs Jepp?' – a genuine curiosity in his voice.

'Yes.'

'I met her one day about three years ago. Laurence introduced me. A fine old lady. Wonderful for her age. Quite excellent. Do you see much of her?'

'I saw her last Easter,' Caroline said, 'she was grand.'

'Yes, she is grand. She doesn't visit London, of course?'

'No,' Caroline said. 'That must have been her last trip when you met her. She hasn't been to London since.'

'She doesn't care for the Hampstead ménage?'

'Well, she's an independent soul,' said Caroline absently.

She had only half taken in the Baron's chatter, although he continued to speak of Louisa.

'I must get in touch with Laurence first thing,' Caroline repeated. 'Mrs Jepp isn't on the phone. I'll send a wire. Oh, Willi! – those voices, it was Hell!'

Now, lying awake in the dark, Caroline recalled the conversation, regretting that she had shown such a supine dependence on the Baron. More and more she thought, 'I should have stayed at home and faced whatever was to be faced.' She knew she had tough resources. And as she tormented herself, now, into confronting her weakness, painfully she recollected the past hour; some of the talk which she had let slip so drowsily through her mind came back to her. It had struck her in passing that the Baron had seemed extraordinarily interested in Laurence's grandmother. He was the last person one would expect to have remembered – and by name – an undistinguished old lady to whom he had been introduced casually three years ago. Mrs. Jepp was not immediately impressive to strangers, was not at all the type to impress the Baron.

Through the darkness, from beside the fireplace, Caroline heard a sound. *Tap*. The typewriter. She sat up as the voices followed:

The Baron had seemed extraordinarily interested in Laurence's grandmother. He was the last person one would expect to have remembered – and by name – an undistinguished old lady to whom he had been introduced casually three years ago. Mrs. Jepp was not immediately impressive to strangers.

Caroline yelled, 'Willi! Oh, my God, the voices . . . Willi!'

Through the wall she heard him stir.

'Did you call, Caroline?'

Eventually he shuffled in and switched on the light.

Caroline pulled the bulky borrowed dressing-gown over her shoulders, her eyes blue and hard with fright. She had grasped the rosary which she had tucked under the cushion at her head. Her fingers clung shakily to the beads as a child clings to its abracadabra toy.

'*My* dear Caroline, what a charming picture you make! Don't move for a second, don't move: I am trying to recall – some moment, some scene in the past or a forgotten canvas – One of my sister's friends perhaps – or my nurse. Caroline, my dear, there is no more exquisite sight than that of a woman taken unawares with a rosary.'

Caroline slung the beads on the post of a chair. The thought flashed upon her, 'He is indecent.' She looked up at him sharply and caught him off guard; his mouth and eyes drooped deadly tired, and he was resisting a yawn. She thought, 'After all, he is kind; it was only a pose.'

'Tell me about the voices,' he said. 'I heard nothing, myself. From what direction did they come?'

'Over there, beside the fireplace,' she answered.

'Would you like some tea? I think there is tea.'

'Oh, coffee. Could I have some coffee? I don't think I'm likely to sleep.'

'We shall both have some coffee. Stay where you are.'

Caroline thought, 'He means that he isn't likely to sleep, either.' She said, 'I'm awfully sorry about this, Willi. It sounds so foolish, but it really is appalling. And you must be dead tired.'

'Coffee and aspirins. *My* Caroline, you are not to apologize, I am delighted –'

But he could hardly conceal his sleepiness. As he returned bearing their coffee, with a bottle of brandy on a tray, he said, as one who keeps the conversation flowing, notwithstanding a tiger in the garden, 'You must tell me all about the voices.' He saw her removing the cotton-wool plugs from her ears, but pretended not to notice. 'I have always believed that disembodied beings inhabit this room,' he went on, 'and now I'm sure. Seriously, I'm sure – indissuasibly convinced, Caroline, that you are in touch with something. I do so wish I had been able to give you some phenobarbitone, an excellent sedative; or something to make you sleep.

But of course I shall sit up with you, it's nearly five already...'

He said no more about hallucinations, by which Caroline understood that he now really believed that she was crazy. She sipped her coffee submissively and jerkily, weeping all the time. She told him to leave her.

'Of course not. I want to hear about the voices. It's most intriguing, really.'

She felt better for the effort to describe what had happened, although the fact gnawed at her that the Baron was finding the episode a strain and a nuisance. But ruthlessly, in her own interest, she talked on and on. And as she talked she realized that the Baron was making the best of it, had resigned himself, was attending to her, but as one who regards another's words, not as symbols but as symptoms.

He got out of her that the clicking of the typewriter always preceded the voices, and sometimes accompanied their speech. How many voices there were, she could not say. Male or female? Both, she told him. It was impossible to disconnect the separate voices, because they came in complete concert; only by the varying timbres could the chorus be distinguished from one voice. 'In fact,' she went on, wound-up and talking rapidly, 'it sounds like one person speaking in several tones at once.'

'And always using the past tense?'

'Yes. Mocking voices.'

'And you say this chorus comments on your thoughts and actions?'

'Not always,' said Caroline, 'that's the strange thing. It says "Caroline was thinking of doing this or that" – then sometimes it adds a remark of its own.'

'Give me an example, dear. I'm so stupid – I can never grasp –'

'Well,' said Caroline, unwhelming herself of a sudden access of confidence in the Baron's disinterestedness, 'take tonight. I was dropping off, and thinking over my conversation with you –

'– as one does –' she added,

'– and it drifted to my mind how you had remembered meeting Laurence's grandmother; I thought it strange you should do so. Next thing, I heard the typewriter and the voices. They repeated my thought, something like, "It came to her that the Baron" – you know we always call you the Baron, " – that the Baron had been extraordinarily interested in Laurence's grandmother." That's what the voices said. And then they added something to effect that the Baron was the last person who would remember, and remember by name, an old woman like Mrs Jepp merely from a passing introduction three years ago. You see, Willi, the words are immaterial –'

'You're mad,' said the Baron abruptly.

Caroline felt relieved at these words, although, and in a way because, they confirmed her distress. It was a relief to hear the Baron speak his true mind, it gave her exactly what she had anticipated, what seemed to her a normal person's reaction to her story. Fearing this, she had been purposely vague when, earlier in the evening, she had explained her distress: 'A typewriter followed by voices. They speak in the past tense. They mock me.'

Now that she had been more explicit, and had been told she was mad, she felt a perverse satisfaction at the same time as a suffocating sense that she might never communicate the reality of what she had heard.

The Baron hastily recovered. 'I use "mad" of course in the colloquial sense. In the way that we're *all mad*, you know. A little crazy, you know. Amongst ourselves, I mean – the intelligentsia are all a little mad and, my dear Caroline, that's what makes us so nice. The sane are not worth noticing.'

'Oh, quite,' said Caroline. 'I know what you mean.' But she was wondering, now, why he had spoken so viciously: 'You're mad!' – like a dog snapping at a fly. She felt she had been tactless. She wished she had chosen to cite a different example of the voices.

'Someone is haunting me, that's what it is,' Caroline said, hoping to discard responsibility for offending the Baron.

He seemed to have forgotten his role as the intrigued questioner; his air of disinterested curiosity was suspended while he told Caroline exactly why and how Mrs Jepp had impressed him. 'You see, she is a character. So small and yet her strength – her aged yet vivid face. So dark, so small. I could never forget that face.'

With surprise, Caroline thought, 'He is defending himself.'

'And she looked so debonair, my dear, in a deep blue velvet hat. Her brown wrinkles. Quite a picture.'

'Three years ago, was it, Willi?'

'Almost three years – I remember it well. Laurence brought her into the shop, and she said, "What a lot of books!"

He gave an affectionate chuckle, but Caroline did not join him. She was thinking of Louisa Jepp's last visit to London, three years ago. Certainly, she did not possess her blue hat at that time, Caroline was acquainted with all Louisa's hats. They were purchased at long intervals, on rare occasions. And only last Easter, Caroline had accompanied the old lady to Hayward's Heath where they had spent the afternoon, eventually deciding on that blue velvet hat which had so pleased Louisa that she had worn it on every occasion since.

'A blue hat?' said Caroline

'My dear, believe it or not, a blue, I recall it distinctly. Blue velvet, curling close to her head, with a fluffy black feather at the side. I shall never forget that hat nor the face beneath it.'

That was the hat all right.

In the face of the Baron's apparent lie – to what purpose? – and the obvious fact that her account of the voices had somehow provoked it, Caroline began to gather her own strength. The glimmering of a puzzle distinct from her own problem was a merciful antidote to her bewilderment. She kept her peace and sipped her coffee, knowing that she was delivered at least from this second mockery, the Baron posing as a credulous sympathizer, his maddening chatter about psychic phenomena, while in reality he waited for the morning, when he could hand her over to Laurence or someone responsible. The Baron might think her mentally unhinged, but by a mercy she had made it clear, though quite unintentionally, that her condition was dangerous for him. In fact, she had forced him to take her seriously, to the extent that he made excuses for himself and lied.

about the **author**

Muriel Spark

D ame Muriel Spark was born Muriel Camberg in
Edinburgh in 1918. Her father was Jewish; her
mother was born in Hertfordshire 'with eyes of an
almost gypsy blackness'. She attended James Gillespie's
School for Girls, the model for the Marcia Blaine School
in *The Prime of Miss Jean Brodie*, Spark's most famous
and enduringly popular work. In 1937, she married
Sydney Oswald Spark and they moved to Africa where a
son, Robin, was born. The marriage soon failed but due
to wartime restrictions on travel Spark was not able to
return to Britain until 1944. In 1947, in London, she
became secretary of the Poetry Society and edited the
Poetry Review but she was sacked two years later. Her
first book was a collection of poetry, after which she
published studies of Wordsworth, Mary Shelley, and
Emily Brontë. In 1951, she won the *Observer* short story
competition with 'The Seraph and the Zambesi'. *The
Comforters*, published in 1957, was the first of 21 novels,
which include *Memento Mori*, *A Far Cry from*

Kensington, The Girls of Slender Means, Loitering with Intent and *Aiding and Abetting*. Her autobiography *Curriculum Vitae* appeared in 1992. She has won numerous awards, including the James Tait Black Memorial Prize, the Italia Prize, the David Cohen Literature Prize in recognition of a lifetime's literary achievement and, most recently, the Boccaccio Prize. She was elected C.Litt in 1992 and was awarded DBE in 1993. She is an honorary member of the American Academy of Arts and Letters and a Commandeur de l'Ordre des Arts et des Lettres in France. She has lived in New York where she had an apartment in the East Village and wrote for the *New Yorker*, which she still does. For the last ten years she has lived in Italy, in a fourteenth century rectory in the Tuscan countryside with her friend, the artist Penelope Jardine.

fiction titles **by**

Muriel Spark

Novels

Aiding And Abetting (2000); *Reality and Dreams* (1996);
Symposium (1990); *A Far Cry from Kensington* (1988);
The Only Problem (1984); *Loitering with Inten*t (1981);
Territorial Rights (1979); *The Takeover* (1976); *The
Abbess of Crewe* (1974); *The Hothouse by the East River*
(1973); *Not To Disturb* (1971); *The Driver's Seat* (1970);
The Public Image (1968); *The Mandelbaum Gate* (1965);
The Girls of Slender Means (1963); *The Prime of Miss
Jean Brodie* (1961); *The Ballad of Peckham Rye* (1960);
The Bachelors (1960); *Memento Mori* (1959); *Robinson*
(1958); *The Comforters* (1957).

Short Story Collections

The Complete Short Stories (2001); *The Young Man who
Discovered the Secret of Life & Other Stories* (2001) *Open
to the Public* (1997); *The Collected Stories* (1994); *The
Stories of Muriel Spark* (1985).

discussion **points**

1. Why do writers write so often about writers?

2. Though she has not lived in Scotland since she was a teenager, Muriel Spark still says she is 'Scottish by formation'. What evidence of her Scottishness is there in *The Comforters*?

3. Spark has been accused by one critic of 'pointless malice'. Is there any justification for this?

4. The 1950s, during which *The Comforters* was published, has been dubbed the decade of the Angry Young Men, with the likes of Kingsley Amis, Alan Sillitoe, Keith Waterhouse and David Storey in the vanguard. Yet it was the decade when women writers such as Muriel Spark, Doris Lessing, Iris Murdoch and others began to flourish. Is this yet another example of the power of male chauvinism coming to the fore or not?

5. Famously, Muriel Spark is a convert to Catholicism. On the basis of *The Comforters* do you think the Vatican would approve of its new recruit?

6. Spark's prose is often praised as 'spare' and 'poetic' but are these adjectives necessarily compliments to a novelist?

press quotes

on *The Comforters*

'Here is a brilliant first novel gaily dedicated to the proposition that things are not always what they seem – and to its corollary, that a good way of hiding anything is to display it openly.'
– *New York Times*

'Enchanting... The prose is as fine and shiny as a summer day.'
– *New York Herald Tribune*

on Muriel Spark

'Our greatest living novelist.'
– *Evening Standard*

'[Muriel Spark] remains inimitable – surely the most engaging, most tantalising writer we have.'
– *London Review of Books*

'There is no question about the quality of distinctiveness of her writing, with its quirky concern with human nature, and its comedy.'
– *Sunday Times*

similar **reads**

The Ordeal of Gilbert Pinfold by Evelyn Waugh
(Penguin Books; ISBN: 0141180218)
First published in 1957.
Unable to control his fantasies, a well-known author goes on a cruise to Ceylon to recuperate but to his horror the hallucinations only get worse.

The Crack-up and other Stories by F. Scott Fitzgerald
(Penguin Books; ISBN: 0140082093)
First published in 1936.
'All life is a process of breaking down,' says Fitzgerald at the outset of the disturbing title story, 'but the blows that do the dramatic side of the work ... don't show their effect all at once.'

Hemlock and After by Angus Wilson
(House of Stratus Ltd; ISBN: 1842324403)
First published in 1952.
Now woefully neglected, Wilson was one of the most talented writers of his generation. This, his debut novel, features Bernard Sands, a successful novelist

who crowns his glittering career by arranging for the government to fund a home for young writers.

Great Granny Webster by Caroline Blackwood
(Duckworth; ISBN: 0715611909)
First published in 1977.
The insidious effects of an old woman, the embodiment of everything 'correct', on three generations of her family, in whom the recurrence of madness is unrelenting.

The Private Memoirs and Confessions of a Justified Sinner by James Hogg
(Canongate Classics; ISBN: 0862413400)
First published in 1824.
A peculiar blend of mockery, bleak humour and degradation, in which a pious, young man uses the Calvinist doctrine of pre-destination to justify the murder of his brother.

The Book of Job
with an introduction by Louis de Bernières
(Canongate Books Ltd; ISBN: 0862417910)
In many ways, *Job* holds the key to Spark's fiction, asking – and answering – how we can have faith in an omnipotent creator who is apparently responsible for creating evil.

competition

Your chance to win ten contemporary works of fiction signed by their authors.

The *Read Around Books* series was developed by Scottish Book Trust to encourage readers to widen their reading interests and discover writers they had never tried before. Has it been a success? We want to hear from you. Tell us if you have enjoyed this little series or not and if you did, do you have any suggestions for authors who should be included in the series in the future.

Writer to us now with the following information:

Name and address
Email address
Are you a member of a readers' group?
Name of readers' group

Send us the information above and we will enter you into our prize draw to be drawn on 22 August 2003.

Send to:
RAB Draw
Scottish Book Trust
137 Dundee Street
Edinburgh EH11 1BG

scottish **book trust**

What is Scottish Book Trust?

Scottish Book Trust exists to serve readers and writers in Scotland. We work to ensure that everyone has access to good books, and to related resources and opportunities.

We do this in a number of ways:

- By operating the Writers in Scotland Scheme, which funds over 1,400 visits a year by Scottish writers to a variety of institutions and groups
- By supporting Scottish writing through a programme of professional training opportunities for writers
- By publishing a wide variety of resources and leaflets to support readership
- By promoting initiatives such as National Poetry Day and World Book Day
- And through our Book Information Service, providing free advice and support to readers and writers, and the general public.

For more information please visit
www.scottishbooktrust.com

titles **in the series**

Available in the Read Around Books series

Iain Crichton Smith's *Murdo: The Life and Works,*
   by Douglas Gifford

Meaghan Delahunt's *In The Blue House,*
   by Gavin Wallace

Michel Faber's *Under the Skin,* by Mary Firth

Jonathan Falla's *Blue Poppies,* by Rosemary Goring

Janice Galloway's *Clara,* by David Robinson

Andrew Greig's *That Summer,* by Alan Taylor

Anne MacLeod's *The Dark Ship,* by Lindsey Fraser

Maggie O'Farrell's *After You'd Gone,* by Rosemary Goring

Suhayl Saadi's *The Burning Mirror,*
   by Catherine McInerney

Ali Smith's *Hotel World,* by Kathryn Ross

Muriel Spark's *The Comforters,* by Alan Taylor

Alexander Trocchi's *Young Adam,* by Gillian Mackay